What Every Babysitter Should Know

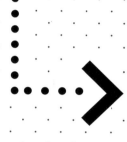

Name Alisha Shelton

St. John Ambulance

Writer: Alexandra Milburn

Indexer: Heather L. Ebbs

Design/Illustrations/Production: Wong + Associates Design Group

Canadian Cataloguing in Publication Data

Main entry under title:
    What every babysitter should know

Includes index.
ISBN 0 – 929006 – 33 – X

    1. Babysitters – Handbooks, manuals, etc.
I. St. John Ambulance. II. Title.

HQ769.5.M45 1992 649' . 1' 0248 C92 – 090466 – 1

First Edition - 1992
Second Edition - 1993
First Impression 1993 - 25,000
Second Impression 1995 - 45,000
Third Impression 1996 - 25,000
Fourth Impression 1997 - 15,000
Fifth Impression 1998 - 15,000
Sixth Impression 1998 - 15,000

Acknowledgements

To the teenagers who told us what they wanted in a course, to those involved with children's services, to moms and dads, St. John Ambulance advisors and babysitting instructors:

Thanks for helping to create this handbook.

St. John Ambulance
National Headquarters

Contents

■ Handbook Activity

CHAPTER FIVE — Kids and Play

CHAPTER SIX — Keeping Kids Safe

CHAPTER SEVEN — Handling Emergencies

CHAPTER EIGHT — First Aid

Notes

....

- feeding the child.
- put the child to sleep
- changing them
- giving them a bath
-

Becoming a Babysitter

START OFF RIGHT

Becoming a Babysitter

99.9

Babysitting is one of the few jobs you can get at a young age and, like any other job, you need to learn how to do it. After taking this course, you'll feel confident that you can keep kids safe, secure and happy.

Why Babysitting?

You may want to become a babysitter for different reasons:

- You'd like to earn some money of your own.
- You want work experience.
- You'd like to prove to yourself and your parents that you're responsible and can be trusted.
- You like taking care of kids.

Before you go any further, let's see if you have what it takes to become a babysitter. Ask yourself the following questions:

Yes   No

1. ☑ ○ Do I like kids? If you like being with kids, they'll know it. They'll also know if you don't like them.

2. ☑ ○ Am I friendly and do I have a sense of humour? Kids like friendly people.

3. ☑ ○ Am I dependable and reliable? When I say I'll be there, I will.

4. ☑ ● Am I responsible? I don't smoke, use drugs or alcohol, or swear around children.

5. ☑ ○ Do I have lots of energy? I won't take on a job if I'm sick or overtired.

6. ☑ ○ Am I flexible? When things don't go as planned, I can adapt and do something else.

7. ☑ ○ Am I honest? If I break something, or if one of the kids hurts himself, I tell the parents as soon as I can.

8. ☑ ○ Do I understand kids and know how to get along with them? I know kids don't always behave and I can handle it.

9. ☑ ○ Can I keep kids safe? I know the common safety hazards and how to prevent injuries.

10. ☑ ○ Do I know what to do in an emergency? I can handle an emergency calmly and quickly.

If you answered yes to all 10 questions, you'll be an ideal babysitter. If you answered no to all 10 questions, maybe babysitting is not for you. If you're somewhere in between, you can become a babysitter, with the help of this course.

Understanding Your Responsibilities

When you're babysitting, you have responsibilities to the parents and to the kids you're looking after. The parents also have responsibilities to you.

The Sitter's Responsibilities

To the kids
- Keep them safe and secure.
- Pay attention to them and be patient with them.
- Feed and comfort them.

To the parents
- Keep their children safe.
- Provide courteous and responsible service.
- Respect the privacy of the parents.

The Parents' Responsibilities

To the sitter
- Give the phone number where they can be reached.
- Provide a list of emergency phone numbers.
- Give information about the children's routines, special needs, favourite toys and bedtimes.

Although it is the parents' responsibility to give you this information, they may not. In that case, it becomes your responsibility to ask.

A Babysitter's Code

Unscramble the underlined words to find out what the babysitter's code is. See page 5 for answers.

1 .... I will be on M E I T.

2 .... I will keep off the O H E P N.

3 .... I will have friends over only if the parents say it's Y O A K.

4 .... I will watch TV only if cleared beforehand, and I will keep it turned W O L so I can hear the kids if they need me.

5 .... I will snack only if invited to do so or bring my N W O.

6 .... I will stay K E A W A.

7 .... I will leave the S O H E U the way I found it.

8 .... I will do everything I can to keep the children F A S E and well cared for.

Setting Your Rates

Before you begin babysitting, you'll need to set your rate of pay. Ask your friends what they charge or ask your neighbours what they pay their babysitters. You may have two rates of pay: one before midnight and one after. Your rate also may increase for each additional child you are asked to keep. The parents may want you to accept a cheque or may want to pay you later. Tell them you want to be paid in cash after each job and don't accept cheques unless you know the people. Be firm about being paid the amount you agreed upon. Prepare yourself for these situations so you'll know what to do.

Finding Work

To find work when you're getting started, ask around. Maybe your neighbours or others you know have heard of sitting jobs. When looking for work, be careful:

- Don't advertise. Anyone could take your name and number. Not all people have good intentions.
- Don't sit for people you don't know or who haven't been recommended. Babysitting for strangers can be risky if you know nothing about them.
- Meet with the family before agreeing to sit for them. Even if you are referred by someone you know, you may not like the situation in the home or the attitude of the parents, or you may just not feel right about it. If so, don't take the job.

The Pre-Job Meeting

Information is a babysitter's best friend. Be prepared for your job by gathering information before you sit. A 20 minute pre-job interview will answer your questions about the family and give you more confidence. It also gives you a chance to get to know the kids. They'll be a lot more relaxed with you on the job if they get to know you beforehand.

If this is your first babysitting job, say that you are really looking forward to sitting for the first time and that you feel confident you can do a good job.

Discuss your rates and come to an agreement on them.

Fill out the Babysitter's Checklist on page 6.

Set up a convenient time to meet the children and family when neither you nor the family is rushed.

Set the tone for the meeting by introducing yourself and explaining your previous babysitting experience and your St. John Ambulance babysitting course.

After the Job

When the parents return, give them a full report. Tell them how the kids behaved, what they ate, what time they went to bed, if anyone called and left a message, or if anything unusual happened.

If the parents don't want to pay you or want to pay you less than the rate you agreed upon, be firm. You provided them with a service and deserve to be paid for your work.

Babysitter's Kit

You may want to prepare a kit for the job. Your kit may contain this handbook and anything else that will make your job easier or more enjoyable. Fill up the kit with things from home that'll help you on the job. See page 5 for answers.

1 ....

2 ....

3 ....

4 ....

5 ....

6 ....

7 ....

8 ....

Code Word

If you think the parents are under the influence of drugs or alcohol or, if for any other reason you don't feel safe having them take you home, take a taxi or have someone pick you up. Pre-arrange a code word with your family that lets them know you need a ride, such as, "Mom, will you bring my purple sweater when you pick me up?"

Answers

A Babysitter's Code, p. 3

1. TIME
2. PHONE
3. OKAY
4. LOW
5. OWN
6. AWAKE
7. HOUSE
8. SAFE

Babysitter's Kit, p. 4

1. Babysitter's Handbook
2. Toys for kids
3. Flashlight
4. Snacks
5. Notebook and pen
6. Clean T-shirt
7. Books for kids
8. Games for kids

Babysitter's Checklist — *Keep by telephone when on the job.*

Name of Family: ....

Address: ....

Cross Street or Description of House Location: ....

....

Phone Number: (H) .... (B) ....

Where parents will be: ....

Phone: ....

Address: ....

Number:

Police ....

Fire ....

Ambulance ....

Poison Information Centre ....

Hospital ....

Number:	*Name:*
Doctor	....
Neighbour	....
Relative	....
Taxi	....

Children:

Name	Age ....
Name	Age ....
Name	Age ....

Special instructions:

Allergies ....

Medications ....

Meals, snacks or feedings ....

Bedtime routines and schedules ....

Playtime ....

Pets ....

Time of return ....

Expected calls or visitors ....

House tour: How to lock doors and windows
Burglar alarms and what could set them off
Discussion of fire plan
Location of • fire extinguisher and smoke detectors
• first aid kit and flashlight
• all possible exits
• extra clothing for children

Caring for Kids

Caring For Kids

The care kids need depends on their age. Caring for kids can be a challenge but, with a little practice, it becomes easier.

How to Pick up a Baby

1. Support the baby's head by placing one hand under his neck, with your fingers supporting his head.
2. Place your other hand under his bottom and pick up.

How to Hold and Carry a Baby

1. Place his head in the bend of your arm and let the baby lie along your forearm and hand. Your other hand is free to hold a stair rail or open a door.
2. Carry the baby in an upright position with his body against your chest and his head resting on your shoulder.

SAFETY Tips

- Babies are easily startled by a sudden loud noise or a jerky movement. Handle gently but securely.

- Babies also have a real fear of falling. Hold close to your body to make the baby feel secure.

How to Bottle-Feed

Warming the bottle
1. Wash your hands before handling the bottle. Babies pick up germs easily and can develop severe diarrhea.
2. Warm the refrigerated formula or mother's milk by putting the bottle or nurser in a pan of warm water.
3. Heat the formula (five to seven minutes) until it feels neither hot nor cold when a few drops are shaken onto your wrist.
4. Check it twice, just to make sure.

Feeding the baby
1. Make sure the baby's diaper is dry and that the baby is warm.
2. Wash your hands again.
3. Settle yourself in a rocking chair or other comfortable spot.
4. Cradle the baby in one arm. Hold the bottle with the other hand so that the baby can suck without having the weight of the bottle against her mouth.
5. Tilt the bottle and place the nipple in the baby's mouth.
6. Check that the nipple is on top of the baby's tongue; sometimes the tongue may get in the way.

7. Keep the bottle tilted so there is always milk in the neck of the bottle. This keeps the baby from swallowing too much air. If the baby swallows a lot of air, she will be uncomfortable unless she can burp.

8. If the baby falls asleep before taking enough milk, change her position or gently stroke her cheek to awaken her.

SAFETY *Tips*

- Warming the formula in a microwave oven is NOT recommended. A microwave will warm the formula unevenly, and the formula will continue to heat after being removed from the oven. Some of the formula could be extremely hot and burn the baby's mouth or some of it could be cold.

- Rubber nipples should not go into the microwave because they continue to heat after removal; plastic bottle liners should not go into the microwave because they can burst while heating.

Burping the baby
Burp the baby halfway through the feeding. When the bottle is finished or the baby refuses to take any more milk, burp her again.

On the shoulder
- Place a clean cloth over your shoulder.
- Hold the baby against your body with her head looking over your shoulder.
- Gently rub or pat her back.

On the lap
- Sit the baby on your lap.
- Support her head and chest with one hand. Your thumb and fingers will be supporting her chin.
- Gently rub or pat the baby's back with your other hand.

Spitting up
- Some babies spit up a mouthful of milk or formula when they are burped. Don't worry about this, just wipe her mouth with the clean cloth from your shoulder.

How to Change a Diaper

1. Gather everything you need before you change the baby: diapers, washcloth or pre-moistened wipes, basin, towel and cream or powder.
2. Wash your hands.
3. Protect change area with changing pad and arrange the changing supplies nearby.
4. Bring the baby to the change area and remove the diaper. If safety pins are used, close them and place them well out of the baby's reach. Put the soiled diaper to the side where the baby can't grab it.
5. Wash the baby's diaper area with the washcloth using warm water. Wash from the front to the back. Dry the baby by patting with a towel. If you notice a rash or any soreness, change the diaper more often, using more cream than usual. Report the rash to the parents when they return.
6. Apply cream or powder according to the parent's directions. If baby powder is used, gently shake some onto your hand,

away from the baby's face, and then pat on diaper area. Shaking the powder directly onto the diaper area may cause the baby to breathe in the fine dust. Try not to get cream or powder on the tabs of disposable diapers. It keeps them from sticking.
7. Put on the clean diaper. Push pins in with points facing the back of the diaper. Use your other hand to protect the baby's skin against a pinprick.
8. Remove any solid material from the diaper by rinsing it in the toilet. Hold onto the diaper and flush the toilet. Wring out the rinsed diaper. If it is a cloth diaper, put it in a diaper pail containing cold water. If it is a disposable diaper, put it in the garbage.
9. Wash your hands.

How to Put a Baby to Bed

1. Follow the parent's instructions for the baby's bedtime routine (story, light on, favourite toys).
2. Lay the baby gently in the crib and speak softly to her. If the parents do not tell you to put the baby in a certain position in the crib, put her on her back or side. If you put the baby on her side, place a rolled blanket or towel behind her for support. Don't use a pillow. Babies can squirm under a pillow and suffocate. Older babies will move or turn to make themselves comfortable no matter which position you put them in.
3. Make sure the crib sides are up and locked and that anything that can harm the baby has been removed from the crib: small toys, pins or anything sharp or small enough to swallow.
4. Close the door gently and check the baby every 15 minutes when you make your rounds. If the family has a baby monitor, turn it on and take the receiver with you when you leave the room.

SAFETY Tips

- Don't lay the baby down in the crib or carriage with a bottle. Babies can choke if a bottle is propped.

St. John Ambulance discourages babysitters from giving tub baths to children under the age of one year. Children younger than one year are harder to handle and may slip or wriggle from your grasp.

SAFETY Tips

- Never leave a child alone in a tub. If left alone, a child could slip and fall, drown, or turn on the hot water and scald himself.

- If the phone rings, wrap the child in a towel and take him with you to answer it, or don't answer the phone. The caller will try again.

- Help the child in and out of the tub, even if he can climb in and out himself, and don't let him stand in the tub. Tubs are slippery and small kids are unsteady on their feet.

How to Give a Bath

1. Gather everything you need before you start: soap, washcloth, towel, shampoo and tub toys.
2. Run the water (use only a couple of inches) before you put the child in. Run cold water first, then hot. Run cold water again to cool the taps. Test the water with your elbow or sprinkle a few drops onto your wrist to make sure it's lukewarm. Don't use oil or bubble bath. Bath oil makes the tub slippery and bubble bath dries the skin.
3. Gently wash the child and then let her have some play time.
4. Shampoo only if the parents request it. Some kids resist having a shampoo. Use a wet washcloth and a little shampoo and gently rub the scalp. Rinse carefully.
5. Wrap in a clean, dry towel and lift out of the tub. Pat child dry and towel-dry hair. Dress warmly.

How to Help with Toileting

Most kids learn to use the toilet sometime after their second birthday.

- Ask the child if he has to use the bathroom and help him if he needs it.
- Ask the parents the word the child uses for toileting and how they are teaching him to do it. Also ask where extra pants and bedding are kept.
- The child may wet or soil his pants accidentally because
  - he is too shy to tell you he has to go to the bathroom,
  - he is nervous because his parents aren't home, or
  - he is just too busy.
- Watch for signs that the child has to use the toilet:
  - crossed legs,
  - hands between legs, or
  - a sudden stop in play.
- Report toileting accidents to the parents when they return, but don't embarrass the child.

Caring for Kids with Disabilities

Kids with disabilities may require extra care. A disability may limit what a child can do or may mean he has to do some things in a different way. For example, a deaf child can enjoy dancing, but has to rely on feeling the music vibrations through the floor, rather than the sound. Kids who are blind or deaf, kids who have to use wheelchairs or crutches to get around and kids with learning or behaviour problems are still just kids.

Meet with the parents and the child beforehand to discuss any extra care. Find out if, like other kids, the child wants things done in a particular way. Get enough information so that you'll be confident on the job.

If you don't think you can handle the responsibility or don't want to, tell the parents and recommend another sitter to them. They'll appreciate your honesty.

Caring for Sick Kids

You can usually tell when a child is sick. She may

- cry or whine constantly,
- refuse to eat or drink,
- show no interest in playing,
- be very quiet,
- complain of a sore tummy,
- feel hot to the touch, or
- vomit.

If the child shows one or more of these signs, get her ready for bed. Keep her warm and comfortable and give her water, apple juice or other clear liquids. Call the parents right away.

If you cannot reach the parents, call the number the parents gave you for medical assistance.

Giving Medicine

If you are asked to babysit a sick child, find out from the parents exactly what kind of care to give. If the child requires any medicine, get the parents to explain the instructions and write them down for you. Before you give the medicine, check that you are giving

1. the right amount,
2. of the right medicine,
3. at the right time,
4. by the right method,
5. to the right child.

Each time you give medicine to the child write down the time, in case the parents want to check that you followed their instructions. You can refuse to give medicine if you're not comfortable doing it. If so, tell the parents before they leave.

SAFETY Tips

- Store or put the medicine container out of a child's reach. Many kids can open childproof caps.

- Don't tell kids that medicine is candy.

Notes

CHAPTER THREE

Kids and Food

Kids and Food

Babies

• • • • • • • • • • • • •

- Older babies usually eat solid foods as well as take a bottle.
- Ask the parents if the baby gets the food first or the bottle first.
- Babies are messy eaters and need a bib.
- Buckle the baby into a high chair before feeding.
- Give the baby only the food the parents suggest and only as much as they suggest.
- Put a small amount of food on a baby spoon and place it well back on the baby's tongue so he won't spit it out.

Toddlers

• • • • • • • • • • • • •

- Toddlers usually have three meals a day, with morning, afternoon and bedtime snacks.
- At this age, kids will be trying new foods, but the foods may still have to be mashed or chopped.

Toddlers may choke very easily on food, especially ones that are hard to chew and swallow. Hot dogs frequently cause choking in very young children.

Pre-Schoolers

• • • • • • • • • • • • •

- Give the child the meals and snacks the parents have left.
- Give the child small servings.
- Don't rush a child who is eating and don't force her to finish everything on her plate.
- Get the older pre-schooler to help you prepare a meal or snack and help with setting the table.
- If you have to prepare a meal, choose at least one serving from each of the four food groups in Canada's Food Guide:
  - fruits and vegetables
  - milk and milk products
  - meat, fish, poultry and alternates
  - breads and cereals

SAFETY Tips

To reduce the risk of choking

- Cut smooth or round foods into smaller pieces lengthwise so they won't get caught in the child's windpipe. Change the round shape of foods such as wieners, sausages and grapes by cutting in half.

- Have the toddler sit quietly when eating. Running, laughing or walking around while eating can cause choking.

SAFETY Tips

If the parents have asked you to prepare a meal, cook safely.

- Know how to turn the stove or appliance on and off.

- Keep pot handles turned toward the back of the stove.

- Don't overheat or leave cooking fats unattended.

Foods That May Cause Choking

Circle the foods that may cause a toddler to choke.
See page 18 for answers.

Meal and Snack Ideas

Evening meal
macaroni and cheese with
tomato slices
peach slices
milk

....
....
....
....
....

Your ideas

....
....
....

....
....
....
....

Snacks
pita bread
bagels
muffins
plain biscuits
cheese chunks
fruit or fruit juice
hard-boiled eggs
peanut butter and
crackers
milk or yogurt

Your ideas

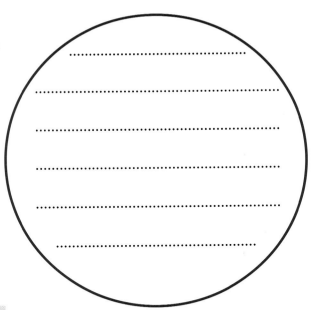

Answers

Foods That May Cause Choking, p. 17
Bacon
Corn
Raw carrots
Raw beans
Chunky peanut butter
Fresh bread
Popcorn
Hard candies
Nuts

Getting Along with Kids

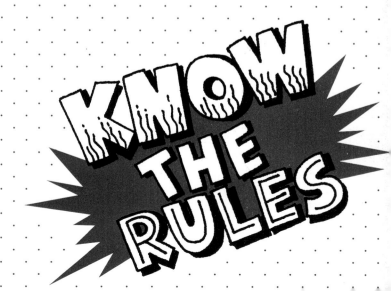

KNOW THE RULES

Getting Along with Kids

Kids can be a challenge. A few guidelines will help you get along with them:
- Be calm and consistent. Kids behave better if you don't get upset.
- Be in control. Once you lose control, it's hard to get it back.
- Be honest and fair. Kids will know if you fake it or when you're not fair with them.

How to Treat Kids

Kids want the same treatment as everyone else: respect, kindness and consideration. Treat them the way you want to be treated.

Think of the babysitters you had as a kid. What did you like and not like about them? The kids you're looking after will probably like and not like the same things.

Let's see how you would treat kids. After each situation, check off the solutions that you think would work. There is not always one right answer for any situation. See page 23 for answers.

Crying

It's 10:30 p.m. and six-month-old Amanda has been asleep for three hours. All of a sudden, she starts to cry loudly. What would you do?

1. ☒ Turn up the TV so you can't hear her.

2. ☑ Try giving her a bottle.

3. ☑ Check to see if her diaper is wet or dirty, or too tight.

4. ☑ Try holding her.

5. ☑ Play peek-a-boo with her.

6. ☑ Try rocking her.

7. ☑ Call parents if she cries longer than 15 to 20 minutes.

8. ☒ Close the door and ignore her.

When a child is crying try to find out what's wrong. Never ignore a baby's cry.

Colic

Three-month-old Michel is crying in his crib. His tummy is tense and his knees are drawn up. What would you do?

1. ☐ Close the door so you can't hear him.

2. ☐ Rub his back or tummy gently.

3. ☐ Pick him up and walk around.

4. ☐ Put him in the carriage and rock it back and forth.

5. ☐ Put him in his carrier and walk around outdoors with him.

6. ☐ Call the parents right away.

Sometimes there is nothing you can do to soothe a colicky baby. You may want to call the parents for advice.

Teething

Jane's cheeks are bright red; she is crying and chewing her blanket. What would you do?

1. ☐ Give her a teething ring.

2. ☐ Give her teething biscuits.

3. ☐ Close the door so you can't hear her.

4. ☐ Bring her out to watch TV.

5. ☐ Try soothing her by rubbing her back.

6. ☐ Carry her around the house and speak to her softly.

7. ☐ Call the parents if you can't settle her down.

A teething baby needs something to chew to relieve the pain. She also needs gentle and soothing treatment.

Shyness

As soon as the Rosenbergs close the door and leave you alone with one-year-old Tricia, she starts to cry. What would you do?

1. ☐ Go to another room of the house and let her cry.

2. ☐ Speak softly and soothingly to her.

3. ☐ Give her a toy from your Babysitter's Kit.

4. ☐ Tell her that her parents will be back later.

5. ☐ Approach her gently and quietly.

6. ☐ Ignore her and read a book.

Sometimes kids feel abandoned when their parents leave. Give them a little time to warm up to you.

Temper Tantrums

Cameron insists on watching a TV show his parents don't want him to see. You tell him "no" firmly and he falls to the floor screaming and kicking. He holds his breath until he turns blue. What would you do?

1. ☑ Make sure he's not close to furniture or a stairway.

2. ☒ Ignore him.

3. ☑ Try to talk him into stopping.

4. ☒ Let him tire himself out.

5. ☑ Try to pick him up and hold him.

6. ☑ Tell him he can watch the TV show.

Although it may be scary for you when a child holds his breath and turns blue, it's not as bad as it looks. He won't be harmed because his body will make sure he begins breathing when he really needs to.

Refuses to Go to Sleep

You put Indra to bed at 8:00 p.m. It's now 9:00 p.m. and she's still awake. What would you do?

1. ☐ Leave her alone. She'll go to sleep when she's ready.

2. ☐ Check your Babysitter's Checklist to make sure you followed her bedtime routine.

3. ☐ Read her an extra story.

4. ☐ Give her a backrub.

5. ☐ Play an active game with her.

Some kids can't settle when their parents are out. The change in routine upsets them. Eventually kids will fall asleep.

Nightmares

Josée begins to scream and call for her mother two hours after you put her to bed. She was having a nightmare and is very frightened. What would you do?

1. ☐ Ignore her. She'll go back to sleep on her own.

2. ☐ Make sure that everything's okay.

3. ☐ Stay with her for awhile.

4. ☐ Leave a light on when you put her back to bed.

5. ☐ Call the parents.

Kids have great imaginations and sometimes cannot tell what's real from what's not. Reassure the frightened child that her dream was not real.

Bedwetting
• • • • • • • • • • • • •

When you go to check on Kalil you notice that his sheets are wet even though he used the toilet before you put him to bed. What would you do?

1. ☐ Scold him for wetting the bed.

2. ☐ Tell him you're going to tell his parents if he does it again.

3. ☐ Help him to clean up.

4. ☐ Change his bed.

5. ☐ Reassure him that it's okay.

6. ☐ Call the parents.

Even though kids use the toilet during the day, it takes longer to learn to stay dry at night. Don't say or do anything to embarrass a child who wets the bed.

Refuses to Share Toys
• • • • • • • • • • • • •

Three-year-old Amy grabs her doll away from her younger sister and hits her over the head with it. She doesn't want to share. What would you do?

1. ☐ Tell her you know it's her toy, but her little sister would like to play with it too.

2. ☐ Try to interest Amy in another toy.

3. ☐ Let Amy keep the doll and try to find another toy for her little sister.

4. ☐ Call the parents right away.

5. ☐ Try to interest both kids in other activities.

Kids go through a stage in which they don't want to share anything. Encourage them to share, but don't be surprised if it doesn't work.

Fighting
• • • • • • • • • • • • •

Two-year-old twins Ronnie and Robbie start slapping and hitting each other. One of them starts to cry. What would you do?

1. ☐ Leave them alone. They can work it out themselves.

2. ☐ Separate them.

3. ☐ Try to interest them in other activities.

4. ☐ Leave them alone in the house and go for a walk.

5. ☐ Don't take sides.

If kids cannot work things out on their own, you may have to get involved. Kids will eventually cool off if they're separated.

Power Struggles
• • • • • • • • • • • • •

Ten-year-old Nam has been testing you all evening. He won't do anything you ask and talks back to you. What should you do?

1. ☐ Try to get him on your side.

2. ☐ Call the parents.

3. ☐ Ask him to show you how to play his favourite game.

4. ☐ Ignore him and let him do what he wants.

5. ☐ Give him as much guidance as you can and pay attention to him.

Older kids may resent having a babysitter because they think they can look after themselves. Be understanding, but be firm.

Answers

· · · · · · · · · · · · ·

Crying, p. 20: 2,3,4,6,7
Colic, p. 20: 2,3,4
Teething, p. 20: 1,2,5,6,7
Shyness, p. 21: 2,3,4,5
Temper Tantrums, p. 21: 1,2,4
Refuses to Go to Sleep, p. 21: 1,2,3,4
Nightmares, p. 21: 2,3,4
Bedwetting, p. 22: 3,4,5
Refuses to Share Toys, p. 22: 1,2,3,5
Fighting, p. 22: 1,2,3,5,
Power Struggles, p. 22: 1,3,5

Notes

. . . .

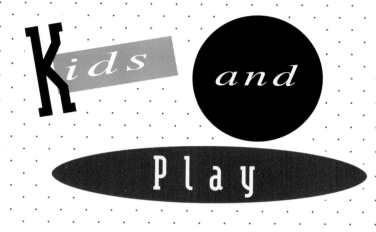

Kids and Play

HAVE FUN

CHAPTER FIVE

Kids and Play

Play at Different Ages

If you know the games and toys that suit a child's age and skill level, you can have fun and help kids learn and discover new things at the same time. Not all kids develop at the same rate. Some are slower and others are faster. All of them go through the same stages of development, but they may reach the stages at different times.

One toy and game is listed to match each age level. Fill in the blanks with your ideas. See page 29 for answers.

Kids learn through play. It's how they learn about themselves, about others and about the world around them.

Benefits of Play

- Stimulates kids to learn.
- Helps kids develop new skills and new behaviours.
- Helps kids discover how to solve problems, how to get along with others and how to express themselves creatively.

One to six months
Infants like to look at and listen to things.

Toys
Colourful mobiles

Games
This little piggy

Six to 12 months
Kids at this age like to do things with their hands and to make noise.

Toys
Big blocks

Games
Pat-a-Cake

One to two years
Young toddlers can walk and are beginning to climb and explore. They're very curious.

Toys
Ride-on toys

Games
Hide-and-Seek

Two to three years
Older toddlers like to imitate adults.

Toys	Games
Puppets	*Dress-up*

Three to five years
Pre-schoolers like active play and playing with others.

Toys	Games
Tricycles	*Catch me*

Six to 10 years
Older kids have a sense of adventure and like to use their imaginations.

Toys	Games
Magic sets	*Craft Kits*

SAFETY Tips

- Always check toys for loose or broken parts and sharp edges.

- Watch kids carefully during play. They may choose toys that aren't appropriate for their age, especially if there is an older brother or sister in the house.

- Watch kids who are playing together. They can get rough with each other.

Toys You Can Make Yourself

You can make these toys at home and put them in your Babysitter's Kit. Kids love to play with new or different toys.

For babies

Make a picture book by cutting out bright pictures and gluing them to cardboard. Punch holes in the cardboard and lace it together. Talk to the baby as you explain the pictures to her.

For toddlers

Make a tube snake from a long string of empty toilet paper rolls. Thread string through six or more rolls that you have decorated with markers in a snakeskin pattern or bright colours, and tape the last tube to the end of the string. As the toddler pulls on it, it will wiggle.

For pre-schoolers

Make masks from paper plates and popsicle sticks. Cut out a butterfly or draw a little girl or little boy face on the plate. Colour it with markers and stick cotton balls or yarn on for decoration. Let the kids come up with their own ideas. Tape the popsicle stick on so the kids can hold the masks up to their faces.

Make a feely bag by putting several different objects in a paper bag. Get the pre-schooler to identify them by touch. Use objects from around the house: eraser, crayon, cotton ball, jar lid or any other objects that have different shapes and textures.

Recipes for Play Materials

Check with parents first if you want to bring your own play materials. They can give you newspapers to protect the floors or furniture from spills and stains.

Playdough

Mix 125 mL (1/2 cup) salt, 250 mL (1 cup) flour and 30 mL (2 tablespoons) cream of tartar. Add 250 mL (1 cup) water, 15 mL (1 tablespoon) vegetable oil and food colouring. Cook on medium heat until dough is right thickness (three to five minutes). Stir constantly. When cool, store in a plastic bag or container with a tight lid.

Play clay

Stir 500 mL (2 cups) baking soda and 250 mL (1 cup) corn starch in a pan. Add 300 mL (1 1/4 cups) cold water. Cook over medium heat, stirring constantly. Add food colouring. When the mixture looks like moist, mashed potatoes, turn onto plate and cover with damp cloth. When cool enough to touch, knead and roll out. Use like modelling clay. Objects will harden overnight.

Rhymes, Chants and Songs

Kids of all ages like to sing and chant. Many of these rhymes have hand and body movements that the kids can do along with you.

I'm a Little Teapot
Ring around the Rosie
Pop Goes the Weasel
This Little Piggy
Pat-a-Cake
Itsy Bitsy Spider

List your favourite rhymes here:

....

....

....

....

....

Answers

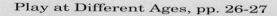

Play at Different Ages, pp. 26-27

One to Six Months
Toys:
Colourful mobiles
Squeeze toys
Stuffed animals
Music boxes
Rattles
Wind-up toys

Games:
This Little Piggy
Peek-a-Boo

Six to 12 Months
Toys:
Big blocks
Toys that pull apart and snap together
Stacking toys
Toy telephone
Pots and pans
Balls

Games:
Pat-a-cake
Peek-a-Boo

One to Two Years
Toys:
Ride-on toys
Push-pull toys
Water toys
Picture books
Simple puzzles

Games:
Hide-and-Seek
Rolling and Catching a Ball

Two to Three Years
Toys:
Puppets
Costumes
Masks
Play dishes
Crayons and paper

Games:
Dress-up
I Spy
Playing store

Three to Five Years
Toys:
Tricycles
Wagons
Skipping ropes
Hula hoops
Roller skates

Games:
Catch Me
Ball

Six to Ten Years
Toys:
Magic sets
Models
Puzzles

Games:
Craft kits
Hobby kits
Cards
Board games
Electronic games

Notes

Keeping Kids Safe

KNOW THE DANGERS

Keeping Kids Safe

When Injuries Are Most Likely to Happen

Injuries happen more often when

- kids are hungry or thirsty and are ready to eat or drink anything. Many poisonings take place just before mealtime.
- kids are tired or the person looking after them is tired.
- kids are rushed or their routines are changed.

Injuries also happen more often when babysitters or less experienced people are looking after kids. This means that you have to be alert while on the job.

Get on the kid's level
Get down on your hands and knees and look around the room. You'll be amazed at what you may find that's dangerous. Remove or secure anything that might be harmful.

Treat kids gently
Don't be rough with kids. Yanking too hard on a child's arm can dislocate his shoulder. Shaking a baby can cause brain damage or death.

How to Prevent Injuries

Most injuries occur to children when they're in the home, and almost half these injuries result from falls. Knowing how to prevent injuries will keep the kids in your care safe and sound.

Add your own ideas to the following lists of how to prevent common childhood injuries.

Falls
- Don't use a baby walker.
- Carry children securely.

- Use safety straps on high chair, infant seat and stroller.
- Hold baby securely while diapering.
- Pull up and lock crib sides.
- Use gates to close off stairways.
- Help kids go up and down stairs.
- Tie kids' shoelaces securely.
- Watch kids in sock feet on bare floors.
- Lock all doors and windows.
- Keep things to climb on away from railings and windows.
- Watch babies on couches or chairs.
- Pick up toys from floor.
- Supervise kids on play structures and in playgrounds.

Can You Think of Others?

....
....
....
....
....

Street accidents
- Watch children as they play outdoors. Play a game of naming the street rules:
- Walk on the sidewalk.
- Cross only at the lights.
- Don't play between parked cars.
- Don't play in the road.
- Be wary of animals.
- Supervise children on tricycles and bicycles.

Can You Think of Others?

....
....
....
....

Burns
- Keep hot liquids away from baby, including tea, coffee and hot chocolate.

- Keep babies away from hot food or hot stove, electrical cords and outlets.
- Run cold water before adding hot water for bathing.
- Check water temperature before placing child in the tub.
- Check temperature of food and milk before feeding.
- Watch kids around wood stoves, fireplaces and radiators.
- Keep lighters, matches and corrosive cleaning products out of reach.
- Use back burners and keep pot handles turned inward on the stove.

Can You Think of Others?

....

....

....

....

....

Choking
- Don't put a baby to bed with a propped bottle.
- Don't tie a pacifier around a baby's neck .
- Don't tie toys to the bed frame.
- Don't let kids run or play while eating.
- Cut food into bite-sized pieces.
- Change the round shape of foods by cutting lengthwise.
- Pick up any small objects that can be swallowed: small toys, stones, buttons or beads, pins or pieces of balloons or plastic bags.
- Check toys for small removable parts.

- Can You Think of Others?

....

....

....

....

....

Smothering
- Don't let the cat sleep with the baby.
- Don't use a pillow in an infant's crib.
- Don't lay an infant on a water bed.
- Keep plastic bags (grocery bags, dry-cleaning bags) away from babies and small children.

Can You Think of Others?

....

....

....

....

....

Poisoning
- Don't let kids eat parts of plants.
- Put all cleansers, bleaches and detergents out of the child's reach.
- Check the bathroom for any medications or vitamins and put them out of reach.
- Put hair sprays, perfumes and alcohol out of reach.
- Know the hazardous product symbols.

Can You Think of Others?

....

....

....

....

....

Drowning
- Supervise children at bath time.
- Supervise swimming or pool activities.
- Close the toilet lid and diaper pail.

Can You Think of Others?

....

....

....

....

....

Hazardous Product Symbols

	Danger	Warning	Caution
Poison	☠	☠	☠
Flammable	🔥	🔥	🔥
Explosive	💥	💥	💥
Corrosive	⚗	⚗	⚗

Beside each product, write down what the symbol means. The first one is done for you. See page 38 for answers.

3 _Danger Poison_

1 _Warning: Corrosive_

4 _Extarning Explosive_

2 _Danger Flammable_

Safety Hazards

Circle all the safety hazards in each situation. See page 38 for answers.

Kitchen

Playground

nswers

Hazardous Product Symbols, p. 34

1. Warning: Corrosive
2. Danger: Flammable
3. Danger: Poison
4. Warning: Explosive

Safety Hazards, pp. 35-37

Handling Emergencies

KEEP COOL

Handling Emergencies

While you're babysitting, you may be faced with an emergency. An emergency is a sudden need for immediate action. It may be either a medical emergency, such as the child falling and losing consciousness, or a household emergency such as a gas leak.

Discuss with the parents at the pre-job meeting what to do in an emergency. If you're prepared, you'll lose your fear of the situation and won't panic. Keep cool so you'll remember what you've learned and be able to put it into practice.

Fire
• • • • • • • • • • • • •

If fire breaks out
1. Remain calm.
2. Get the kids and get out of the house immediately.
3. Go to the nearest neighbour to call the fire department.

If your clothes catch fire
1. Stop whatever you are doing.
2. Drop to the floor and cover your face with your hands.
3. Roll over and over until the fire goes out.

If the child's clothes catch fire
1. Don't let the child run.
2. Wrap the child in a blanket or coat.
3. Roll the child over and over on the floor.

If there is smoke in the house
1. Stop whatever you are doing.
2. Drop to the floor.
3. Crawl underneath the smoke to where the air is clearer.
4. Get the kids and get out.

If the grease in a pot or pan catches fire
1. Smother flame by putting a lid on the pan.

2. Turn off the heat.
3. Watch that your clothing doesn't catch fire.
4. Never carry a burning pan out of a house and never use water on grease fires.

If you become trapped
1. Close the doors between you and the smoke.
2. Stuff the cracks and under the door with a towel, blanket or clothing.
3. Cover air vents.
4. Have the children lie on the floor, with their faces down. Cover faces with wet cloths if possible.
5. Call for help from a window and signal with a flashlight or by waving with a sheet, towel or sweater, or anything easily seen by someone outside.

Prowler
• • • • • • • • • • • • •

If you suspect that someone is outside, who has no reason for being there, or if you hear someone trying to break into the house

1. Call the police.
2. Stay inside and make sure all doors and windows are locked.
3. Reassure the kids if they are awake.

Unexpected Visitor
• • • • • • • • • • • • •

1. If it is someone you know or someone the parents told you to expect, open the door.
2. If it is a stranger, speak through the window or door. Say the parents are busy and offer to take a message. Do not let the person in.
3. If the stranger does not go away, call the police.

Emergency Procedure

If you are faced with an emergency, take the following steps:

Keeping in mind the emergency procedure, complete the comic strip by filling in the balloons.

AT THE NEIGHBOUR'S...

1. Get the child and get out.
2. Keep calm and reassure the child.
3. Call the emergency number.
4. Give address, telephone number and your name.
5. State what the emergency is.
6. Don't hang up until told to do so.
7. Follow the instructions given.

Nuisance Calls
• • • • • • • • • • • • • •

1. Offer to take a message.
2. Don't tell the caller that you are the babysitter and you're alone.
3. Hang up if the caller becomes a nuisance.
4. If you feel threatened, call the police.

Power Failure
• • • • • • • • • • • • • •

During the day
1. If you're using the stove, turn it off.
2. Locate the flashlight in case the power failure lasts until dark.

During the night
1. Reassure the children.
2. Turn on the flashlight.
3. Call the parents.

If You Smell Gas
• • • • • • • • • • • • • •

1. Check to see that stove burners are turned off.
2. Take the kids and get out of the house.
3. Call the emergency number for your area.
4. Stay outside until all the fumes are gone and the leak has been repaired.

If a Water Pipe Breaks
• • • • • • • • • • • • • •

1. Put the child in a safe, dry area.
2. Don't touch any wires or light switches.
3. Call the parents.

Storms and High Winds
• • • • • • • • • • • • • •

1. Close all windows and doors securely.
2. Stay indoors and reassure the children if they are frightened.
3. If there is thunder and lightning, shut off TV and computer.
4. Locate a flashlight in case power goes off.

Locked out of House (Babysitter)
• • • • • • • • • • • • • •

1. Go to nearest neighbour for help.
2. Call parents.
3. If the kids are inside the house and you cannot reach the parents or get back into the house with a neighbour's help, call the police.

Locked in Bathroom (Child)
• • • • • • • • • • • • • •

1. Call child to door and encourage him to turn door handle or lock.
2. Call a neighbour, parents or the police if child cannot unlock door.

First Aid

In this chapter, you'll learn First Aid for common childhood injuries. To become qualified in giving First Aid, sign up for a St. John Ambulance certified First Aid course.

This chapter does not replace a First Aid course

First Aid

EMERGENCY SCENE

A child who is hurt may be scared and crying. Reassure him, let him know you understand that he's hurt, and that you're there to help him.

You can probably handle many minor injuries by yourself. Other injuries may be too serious for you to handle on your own, and you'll need to get help. Follow these steps in an emergency:

1. Look, listen and smell for clues.

2. If there is any danger to you or the child, make the area safe if you can.

3. Tap the child on the shoulders and in a loud voice ask, "Are you O.K.?" If there is no response, call for help and call the parents.

4. Check for breathing, bleeding and then injuries.

5. Give first aid if you know how.

Help the babysitter in this emergency scene.

What does he see, hear and smell?

....

How can he make the area safe?

....

What would he do next?

....

To find out the first aid to give at this scene, see page 56.

Artificial Respiration (AR) – Infant

1. If not alone, send someone to call for medical help.

2. Lay the non-breathing infant on his back. Tilt the head by pushing back on the forehead while lifting the chin with 2 fingers under the jaw.

3. Look, listen and feel for signs of breathing.

4. If the infant isn't breathing, make a tight seal over his mouth and nose and give 2 slow breaths. Blow just enough to make the chest rise. Look, listen and feel for air movement between breaths.
   • If the baby's chest doesn't rise, retilt the head and try again.
   • If his chest still doesn't rise, give first aid for Choking Infant (see page 47).

5. Check the pulse on the inside of the baby's arm just above the elbow for 5–10 seconds.

6. If there is a pulse, give 1 breath every 3 seconds.

   If there is no pulse, start cardiopulmonary resuscitation (CPR), but only if you have been taught. Otherwise, continue AR.

7. If alone, continue AR for 1 minute then carry the baby with you to call for medical help while doing AR.

8. Continue AR until the infant starts breathing or until medical help takes over.

Artificial Respiration (AR) – Child

• • • • • • • • • • • • • •

1. If not alone, send someone to call for medical help.

2. Lay the non-breathing child on his back and tilt the head backward.

3. Look, listen and feel for signs of breathing.

4. If the child isn't breathing, seal his mouth and pinch his nostrils. Give 2 slow breaths. Blow just enough to make the child's chest rise. Look, listen and feel for air movement between breaths.
   • If his chest doesn't rise, retilt the head and try again.
   • If his chest still doesn't rise, give first aid for Choking Child (see page 48).

5. Check the pulse on the side of the child's neck just to the right or left of the Adam's apple, for 5–10 seconds.

6. If there is a pulse, give 1 slow breath every 3 seconds. If there is no pulse, start CPR, but only if you have been taught. Otherwise, continue AR.

7. If alone, continue AR for 1 minute, then call for medical help.

8. Continue AR until the child starts breathing or until medical help takes over.

Choking – Infant

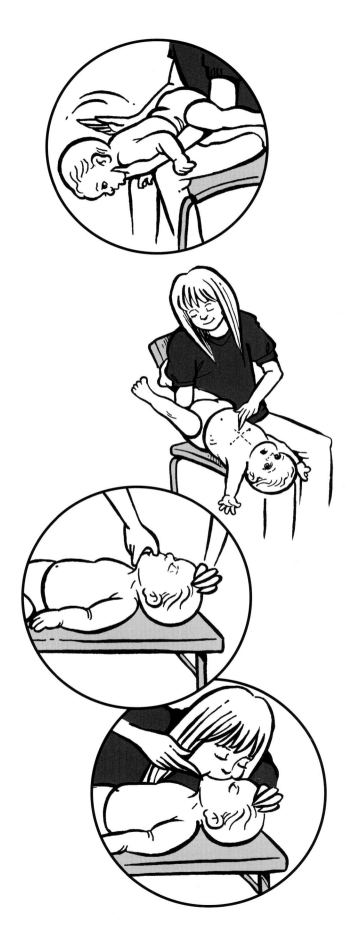

1. Start first aid immediately when you see or hear an infant
   - choking on an object,
   - having serious difficulty breathing,
   - making high-pitched noises, or
   - turning "blue" (lips).

2. To clear the infant's airway, give 5 quick, distinct blows on the back between the shoulder blades. Use the heel of your hand with some force.

3. If the infant still isn't breathing, turn him quickly onto his back and give 5 quick, distinct thrusts to his chest. For chest thrusts, use 2 fingertips on the breastbone, one finger-width below the nipple line.

4. Repeat the back blows and chest thrusts until the airway is cleared or the infant goes unconscious.

5. If the infant goes unconscious, call out for someone to get medical help. If alone, give first aid for 1 minute before calling for medical help. Open the baby's mouth, grasp his tongue with your thumb and lift his chin with your fingers under his jaw. Look for an object and remove only what you see.

6. If the baby doesn't start to breathe, try to give 2 breaths. If his chest doesn't rise, retilt the head and try again.

7. If his chest still doesn't rise, continue with back blows, chest thrusts, mouth checks, and attempt to give AR. (Retilt the head if the chest does not rise). Continue until the object is forced out.

For breathing emergencies caused by an illness or an allergic reaction, do not follow the steps for choking, but get medical help immediately.

Choking – Child

1. If the child can speak, breathe or cough, tell him to cough the object out.

2. If the child can't speak, breathe or cough, stand behind him and find the top of his hip bones with your hands. Slide the fingers toward the midline until they meet.

3. Make a fist with one hand and place it midline, with your thumb against the child's abdomen just above the other hand.

4. Grasp your fist and press inward and upward quickly and forcefully. Continue these abdominal thrusts until the object is forced out or until the child goes unconscious.

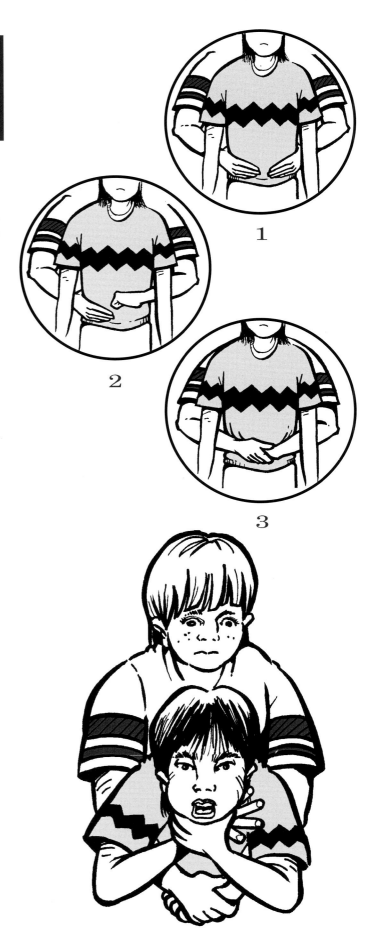

1

2

3

Any infant or child who has been given first aid for choking should be seen by a doctor.

5. If the child goes unconscious, call out for someone to get medical help. Ease the child to the floor or ground. If alone, give first aid for 1 minute before calling for medical help. Open his mouth. Grasp his tongue with your thumb and lift his chin with your fingers under his jaw. Look for the object and remove only what you can see.

1

2

6. If the child doesn't start to breathe, try to give 2 breaths.
   • If his chest doesn't rise, retilt his head and try again.
   • If the chest still doesn't rise, kneel across his legs. Use your hands to find the top of his hip bones with your thumbs pointing to the midline. At the midline, place the heel of one hand slightly above your thumb. Place the other hand on top—fingers raised. Give up to 5 quick, inward and upward thrusts. Check for an object in the child's mouth and try to give him AR.
   • If the child's chest doesn't rise, continue the abdominal thrusts, mouth checks and attempt to give AR. (Retilt the head if the chest does not rise). Continue until the object is forced out.
   • If the child's chest rises, continue with AR until the child starts breathing or medical help takes over.

Wounds and Bleeding

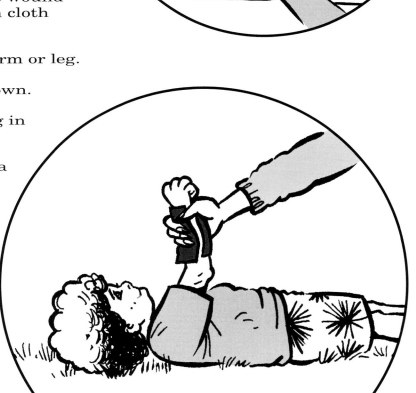

Minor scrapes

1. Wash your hands.

2. Don't cough, breathe over or touch the open wound.

3. Clean the wound with soap and water. Pat dry.

4. Cover the wound with a dressing and tape it in place.

Severe bleeding

1. Apply pressure to the wound over a dressing, clean cloth or towel.

2. Elevate the injured arm or leg.

3. Get the child to lie down.

4. Bandage the dressing in place.

5. Cover the child with a blanket.

6. Call for medical help.

Note:

If first aid gloves are handy, use them whenever you have to handle blood or other body fluids.

Do not stop a nosebleed caused by a blow to the head, but call for medical help immediately.

Nosebleeds

1. Get the child to lean forward and pinch the soft part of his nose for 10 minutes.

2. If the bleeding continues or starts again, call for medical help.

3. Tell the child not to blow the nose for a few hours

How to make:
A **Cold Compress** - soak a towel in cold water and wring out.
An **Ice Bag** - fill a plastic bag with ice and wrap in a towel.

Bruises

1. Sit or lay the child down.

2. Elevate the arm or leg that is bruised.

3. Apply a cold compress or ice bag for 15 minutes, then take it off for 15 minutes. Repeat until the pain goes away.

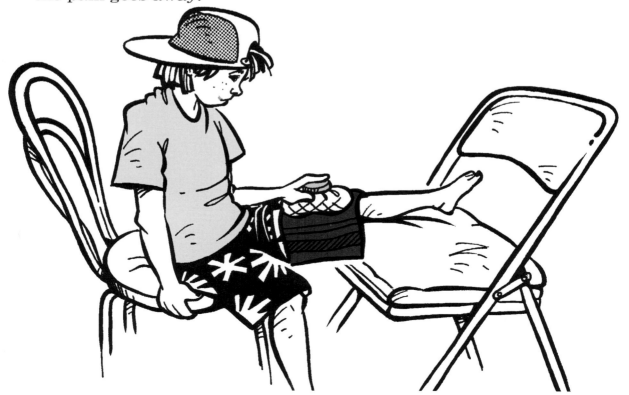

Bump on the Head – Conscious Child

1. When the child has had a bump on the head, but you don't think it could have caused a neck or back injury, keep her at rest.

2. Put a cold compress or ice bag (15 minutes on, 15 minutes off) on the bump to relieve pain and swelling.

3. Check the child often for:
   • loss of consciousness or memory (ask her what her name is and where she lives),
   • a change in her breathing, pulse or skin temperature,
   • headache, nausea or vomiting.

4. If you see any of these signs or symptoms, now or later, get medical help immediately.

Neck or Back Injury – Conscious Child

1. You should suspect a head or back injury if the child was hit with a lot of force, such as by a car; or has fallen from a height.

2. Tell the child to keep still.

3. Call for medical help immediately.

4. Steady and support the child's head and neck in whatever position you found him.

5. Check that he keeps breathing. Give AR if needed as on page 46, but DO NOT TILT the head back. Instead, push the jaw upwards just below the ears.

6. Cover the child with a blanket.

Burns

Heat burns

1. Put the burned area in cool water, if possible. If not, soak a clean towel in cool water and put it on the burn.

2. When the burned area feels better, cover with a dressing or clean cloth.

3. Call for medical help.

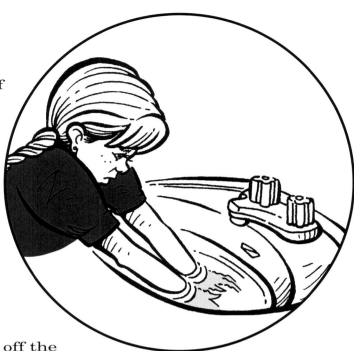

Chemical burns

1. Flush a liquid chemical off the child's skin immediately with cool water. Keep flushing for 10–15 minutes.

2. Brush a dry chemical off the child's skin with a dry cloth. Then flush with cool water for 10–15 minutes.

3. Cover the burn with a dressing or clean cloth.

4. Call for medical help.

Mild sunburn

1. Bring the child indoors or into the shade and keep him there the rest of the day.

2. Cover the burn with a cool, wet towel.

3. If there is any sunburn ointment or cream in the house, you may use this on the burn.

Electrical burns (shock)

1. Unplug the appliance cord that caused the burn so that you or others will not be injured.

2. Check to see if the child is breathing:
   - If he is breathing, apply a burn dressing or clean cloth to the burn.
   - If he isn't breathing, call out for help and begin AR.

3. Call for medical help.

Poisoning

Swallowed

1. Try to find out what was swallowed, how much was swallowed and when it happened.

2. Call the Poison Information Centre 24-hour number in your area for directions or get medical help.

3. Follow the directions you're given.

Inhaled

1. Move the child to fresh air and call for medical help.

2. If the child is breathing, watch that she keeps on breathing.

3. If the child isn't breathing, start AR.

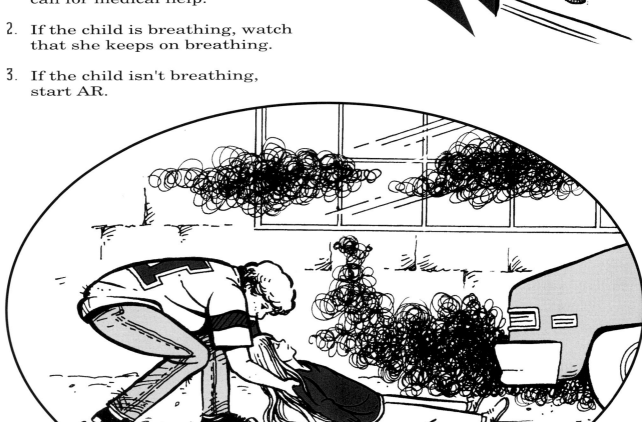

Absorbed through the skin

1. Brush off dry (dust or powder) poison with a dry cloth.

2. Flush the area with lots of cool running water.

3. Flush liquid poison immediately while you remove the child's clothing.

4. Wash the child's skin with soap and water and rinse.

5. Call for medical help.

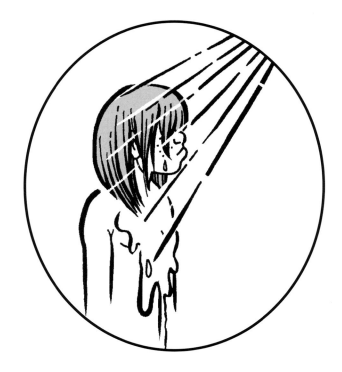

Bee, wasp and hornet stings

1. Without squeezing the stinger, scrape it from the child's skin.

2. Put rubbing alcohol or a paste of baking soda and water on the sore area.

3. If the child was stung in the mouth, give him a piece of ice to suck.

Allergic reaction

An allergic reaction to a bee sting may cause death. Call for medical help immediately if the child has any of the following:
- sick stomach
- breathing difficulties
- vomiting
- hives
- swelling around eyes, mouth and throat
- unconsciousness

While waiting for help:
- If the child has medication that has been prescribed for his allergic reaction, help him to take it.
- Check that he keeps breathing. Give him AR if he stops breathing.
- Keep him at rest.

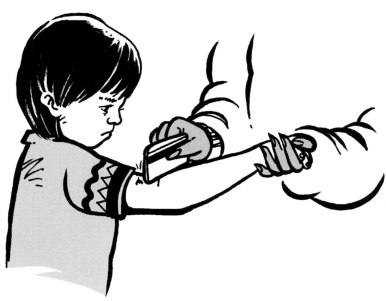

Animal or Human Bites

1. Wash the bite with soap and water and rinse.

2. If the skin is broken
   • get medical help immediately,
   • apply a dressing and bandage.

Eye Injuries

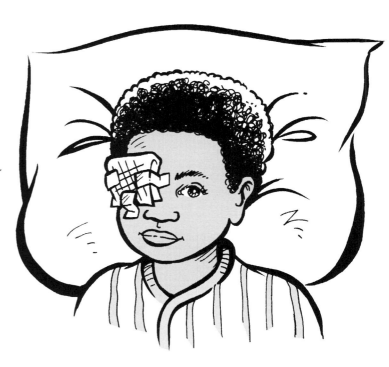

Particle stuck to the eyeball
1. Lay the child down gently, protecting his head.

2. Don't remove the particle.

3. Cover the injured eye loosely with a light dressing.

4. Tape the dressing in place and don't put pressure on the eye.

5. Call for medical help.

Loose particle in the eye
1. Wash your hands.

2. Spread the child's eyelids apart with your thumb and finger.

3. If the particle is not on the black or coloured part of the eye, gently remove it with the moistened corner of a tissue or clean cloth.

4. If you cannot find or easily remove the particle, give first aid for a particle stuck to the eyeball.

Chemical burn to the eye

1. Protect the uninjured eye.

2. Flush the injured eye immediately with cool running water for at least 10 minutes.

3. Cover the injured eye with a light dressing and tape in place.

4. Get medical help immediately.

Object in Ear or Nose

1. Don't try to get the object out.

2. Calm the baby if he is upset.

3. Call for medical help.

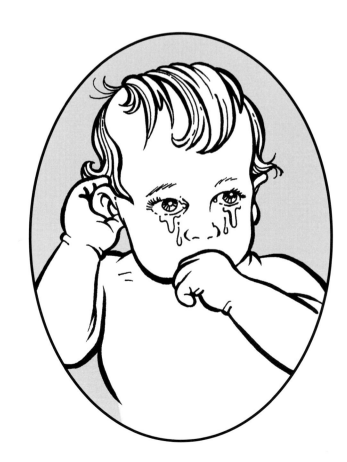

Fever Convulsions

When a child has a convulsion, it may be caused by a high fever. Look for the following:
- very hot skin
- stiff body
- arched back
- holding of breath
- frothing at the mouth

During a convulsion
1. Protect the child from injury.

2. Don't try to stop the child's movements, and don't try to put anything in the mouth to keep it open.

After the convulsion
1. Check for breathing, and if breathing, place the child as shown below. If not breathing, give AR as shown on page 45 for an infant or on page 46 for a child (age 1 to 8 years).

2. Loosen any tight clothing.

3. Get medical help.

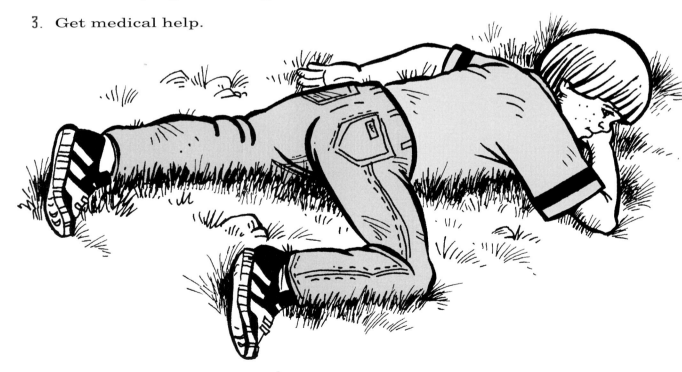

Index

Notes

Notes

· · · · · · · · · · · · ·

Notes

. . . .